The Box

Elspeth Graham
Illustrated by Ian Newsham

Oxford

Mrs Best had a big box.

Pirate
Jack

Mrs Best was a pirate.

The box was her ship.

Poppy was a bear.

The box was her den.

Tom was a footballer.

The box was his goal.

Jo was a princess.

The box was her castle.

Poppy got a book.

"Time for a story," said Mrs Best.

irate ship

inderella.

Big bear

"Where's Kenny?" said Poppy.

Everyone looked for Kenny.

Kenny was asleep.
The box was his bed.